BATMAN
IMPOSTORS

BATMAN IMPOSTORS

DAVID HINE Writer **SCOTT MCDANIEL** Penciller **ANDY OWENS** Inker

DAVID BARON ALLEN PASSALAQUA GUY MAJOR Colorists **TODD KLEIN** Letterer

PETER NGUYEN Cover artist **Batman** created by **BOB KANE**

Mike Marts Michael Siglain Editors – Original Series
Harvey Richards Assistant Editor – Original Series
Ian Sattler Director – Editorial, Special Projects and Archival Editions
Robbin Brosterman Design Director – Books

Eddie Berganza Executive Editor
Bob Harras VP – Editor in Chief

Diane Nelson President
Dan DiDio and **Jim Lee** Co-Publishers
Geoff Johns Chief Creative Officer
John Rood Executive VP – Sales, Marketing and Business Development
Amy Genkins Senior VP – Business and Legal Affairs
Nairi Gardiner Senior VP – Finance
Jeff Boison VP – Publishing Operations
Mark Chiarello VP – Art Direction and Design
John Cunningham VP – Marketing
Terri Cunningham VP – Talent Relations and Services
Alison Gill Senior VP – Manufacturing and Operations
David Hyde VP – Publicity
Hank Kanalz Senior VP – Digital
Jay Kogan VP – Business and Legal Affairs, Publishing
Jack Mahan VP – Business Affairs, Talent
Nick Napolitano VP – Manufacturing Administration
Ron Perazza VP – Online
Sue Pohja VP – Book Sales
Courtney Simmons Senior VP – Publicity
Bob Wayne Senior VP – Sales

BRRDEEE-
BE-DA-
BRREEPP!

New Message
from L'Homme
Qui Rit:
Blue Skies Mall
— 1 PM

WHAT'S WITH THE RAINCOAT, DADDY? IT'S A TOTALLY SUNNY DAY.

FORECAST SAYS 10% CHANCE OF SHOWERS.

DADDY'S NOT A MAN TO TAKE CHANCES WITH THE WEATHER.

YOU BE GOOD FOR MOMMY.

HAVE A GREAT DAY, HONEY.

I'LL TRY.

RESCHEDULE MY AFTERNOON MEETINGS, JENNY. SOMETHING CAME UP.

ALL RIGHT, LISTEN UP. THESE PERPS ARE UNDER THE INFLUENCE OF MIND-ALTERING SUBSTANCES AND THAT'S GOING TO MAKE THEM LIABLE TO RESIST ARREST, BUT THEY'RE ONLY GUILTY OF DISORDERLY CONDUCT, VANDALISM, AND RECKLESS ENDANGERMENT.

KEEP YOUR SIDE ARMS HOLSTERED. NIGHT STICKS ONLY.

LET'S DO THIS THE CIVILIZED WAY.

BUST THEIR HEADS AND CUFF 'EM.

HAHA HAHAHA

HA HA HA HA HA HAH HA HA!

OH, NO!

HA HA HA HA HA HA

SMAKKK

LEAVE IT, MICKY. IT'S JUST A DUMMY.

HAH

HA HA HA HA

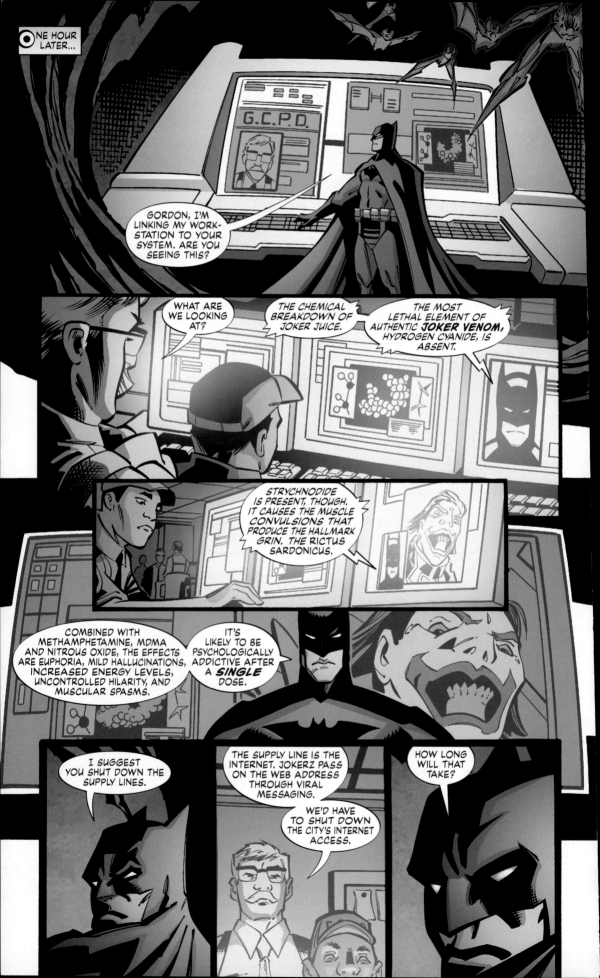

ONE HOUR LATER...

GORDON, I'M LINKING MY WORK-STATION TO YOUR SYSTEM. ARE YOU SEEING THIS?

WHAT ARE WE LOOKING AT?

THE CHEMICAL BREAKDOWN OF JOKER JUICE.

THE MOST LETHAL ELEMENT OF AUTHENTIC **JOKER VENOM**, HYDROGEN CYANIDE, IS ABSENT.

STRYCHNODIDE IS PRESENT, THOUGH. IT CAUSES THE MUSCLE CONVULSIONS THAT PRODUCE THE HALLMARK GRIN. THE RICTUS SARDONICUS.

COMBINED WITH METHAMPHETAMINE, MDMA AND NITROUS OXIDE, THE EFFECTS ARE EUPHORIA, MILD HALLUCINATIONS, INCREASED ENERGY LEVELS, UNCONTROLLED HILARITY, AND MUSCULAR SPASMS.

IT'S LIKELY TO BE PSYCHOLOGICALLY ADDICTIVE AFTER A *SINGLE* DOSE.

I SUGGEST YOU SHUT DOWN THE SUPPLY LINES.

THE SUPPLY LINE IS THE INTERNET. JOKERZ PASS ON THE WEB ADDRESS THROUGH VIRAL MESSAGING.

WE'D HAVE TO SHUT DOWN THE CITY'S INTERNET ACCESS.

HOW LONG WILL THAT TAKE?

"I'M NOT DEAD.

"I'M NOT DEAD.

"I'M NOT DEAD."

JOKERZ RULE

GOOD MORNING, MR. HEATH.

CRAZY TIMES OUT THERE.

INDEED THEY ARE, HENRY, AND MARK MY WORDS, THEY'LL GET CRAZIER YET.

THE POWER IS BACK ON, SIR. YOU CAN USE THE ELEVATOR.

THAT MASK WEIRDS ME OUT. MAKES YOU WONDER WHAT'S *UNDERNEATH*.

WELL, WHY DON'T YOU *ASK* HIM? POLITELY ENQUIRE IF HE'LL VERY KINDLY GIVE YOU A PEEK AT HIS *HORRIBLY DISFIGURED FACE.* I'M SURE HE'LL OBLIGE.

WHAT WAS IT, ANYWAY? FIRE? CHEMICAL BURNS?

I HEARD HE WENT ON A DRINKING BINGE, FORGOT TO FEED HIS DOG FOR A WEEK.

PASSED OUT AND WHEN HE WOKE UP HE FOUND HIS FAITHFUL HOUND HAD EATEN HIS FACE.

YEESH! YOU'RE A SICK MAN, HENRY.

IF YOU DON'T MIND MY SAYING SO, THESE ENTRIES ARE BECOMING A LITTLE REDUNDANT, AREN'T THEY?

APART FROM A FEW MINOR INCIDENTS, THERE WAS ONLY ONE DAY OF CONFLICT BETWEEN GUARDIAN BATS AND JOKERZ.

Impostor Wars: Day 22

I WOULD HAVE THOUGHT "IMPOSTOR SKIRMISH" MIGHT BE MORE APPROPRIATE.

IT ISN'T OVER UNTIL IT'S OVER, ALFRED.

AS YOU SAY...

YOU THINK I'M *OBSESSING* OVER THIS, DON'T YOU?

THE *IMPOSTOR BATMAN* IS A MASS MURDERER WHO IS STILL AT LARGE. THE *IMPOSTOR JOKER* MAY OR MAY NOT HAVE COMMITTED MURDER. HE MOST CERTAINLY INSTIGATED THE RIOTS.

I'M NOT GOING TO LEAVE THIS.

OF COURSE YOU'RE NOT.

I THINK I MAY HAVE SOMETHING.

GOTHAM NEWS--LATEST: BART'S FAIR COMES TO GOTHAM.
PLAY VIDEO

NO BIG SURPRISE. WHEN THE MAYOR APPROVED THE LICENSE FOR THE FAIR, EVERYONE KNEW THIS WOULD HAPPEN.

GOTHAM'S FINEST ARE PREPARED...

...ONE WAY OR ANOTHER.

BY THE TIME THE GAS DISPERSES, THE **BATMAN IMPOSTORS** ARE FLOODING INTO THE FAIRGROUND, ARMED TO THE TEETH AND TAKING NO PRISONERS.

MAYOR HADY HAS A LOT TO ANSWER FOR. I ONLY HOPE, WHATEVER WINSLOW HEATH USED AGAINST HIM, IT WAS WORTH THE BARGAIN.

THE **JOKER IMPOSTORS** CAME UNARMED, BUT THEY DON'T STAY THAT WAY FOR LONG. JUICED TO THE EYEBALLS, THEY IGNORE WOUNDS THAT WOULD INCAPACITATE A NORMAL PERSON, TO SEIZE ARMS FROM THE POLICE, FROM THE GUARDIAN BATS...

...ANYWHERE THEY CAN FIND THEM.

IT APPEARS THERE IS NO SHORTAGE OF WEAPONS IN BARTHOLOMEW FAIR...

HAH HA HA

HA HA HA HA HA

DING!

AS THE MIDNIGHT HOUR STRIKES ON THE FINAL DAY OF THE IMPOSTOR WARS, ALL HELL LETS LOOSE AND CHAOS TRULY REIGNS OVER ALL...

BATMAN: IMPOSTORS, PART FOUR: "LAST MAN LAUGHING"

DAVID HINE: WRITER   SCOTT McDANIEL: PENCILS   ANDY OWENS: INKS
GUY MAJOR: COLORS   TODD KLEIN: LETTERS   HARVEY RICHARDS: ASST. ED.
MIKE MARTS: EDITOR   PETER NGUYEN: COVER   BATMAN CREATED BY BOB KANE

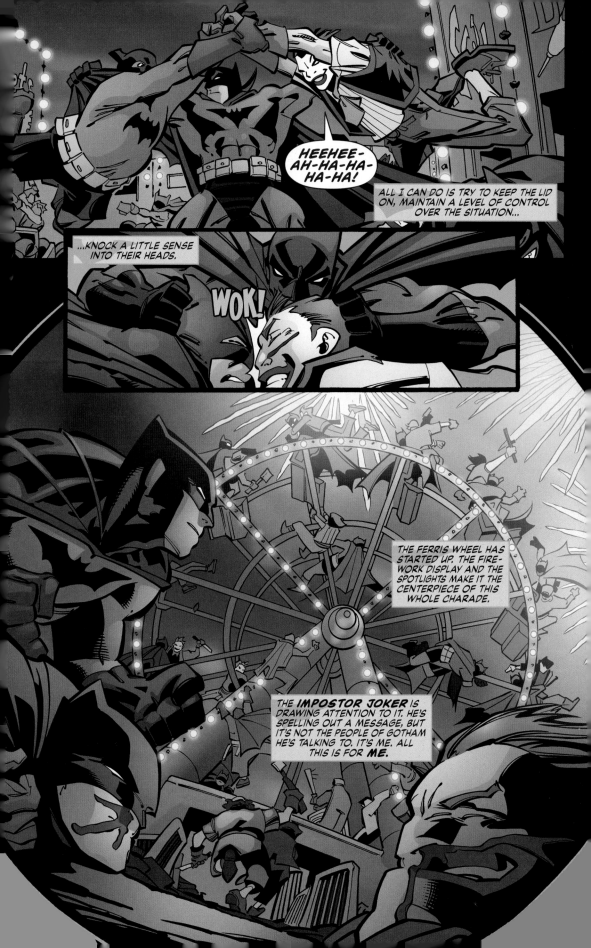

ONE HUNDRED AND SEVENTY-FOUR PEOPLE DIED LAST NIGHT.

THERE WERE OVER ONE THOUSAND ARRESTS.

MOST OF THEM WILL WALK.

THEIR LAWYERS WILL PLEAD TEMPORARY INSANITY, AND WHO WOULD ARGUE WITH THAT?

THE MEDIA WILL BLAME WINSLOW HEATH FOR EVERY-THING.

ONLY WINSLOW HEATH WILL BLAME BATMAN.